NIMROD
A CAVALRY BLACK
from foal to retirement

D1610712

JULIET BLAXLAND

J. A. ALLEN · LONDON

Foreword by

Lieutenant General Sir Barney White-Spunner KCB, CBE

Generations of black horses have served faithfully in The Household Cavalry. They have been helping to guard our kings and queens, and taking part in great ceremonial occasions, since Charles II was restored in 1660. Beyond that they have fought for their country, in the many cavalry battles of the eighteenth century and the Napoleonic Wars, charging at Waterloo, suffering for the empire in Africa and the Middle East, waiting patiently behind the trenches in World War I, and being amongst the last British Army horses to be mobilised when they were sent to Palestine in 1939. Many thousands lost their lives or their health in these wars and they have shown fortitude and bravery every bit as heroic as that of The Household Cavalrymen who rode them.

Today those days of mounted warfare are behind us but the 'Blacks' still mount guard in London, escort Her Majesty The Queen and The Royal Family and play their part in our nation's continuing story. Each one is an individual, a character in their own right, usually loved, always respected, and conscious, in their own unique way, that they are just as important as their people. Please enjoy Juliet Blaxland's charming story of their lives, and learn how a young black horse from a faraway meadow can come to guard The Queen. ᧁᧁ

Lieutenant General Sir Barney White-Spunner KCB, CBE is a former Household Cavalry officer (Blues and Royals), military historian and author.

This is the story of **Nimrod**, one of the big black horses of the Household Cavalry Mounted Regiment, also known as Cavalry Blacks.

The Household Cavalry is composed of the two senior regiments of the British Army: The Life Guards, and The Blues and Royals. The Household Cavalry serves two purposes: to fight for the country and to guard the monarch.

The Household Cavalry Mounted Regiment represents the guard element, whose elaborate ceremonial traditions have evolved from the everyday practicalities of more than 350 years as the monarch's personal bodyguard. Nimrod is one among 250 such horses, and this book illustrates a life typical of any Cavalry Black.

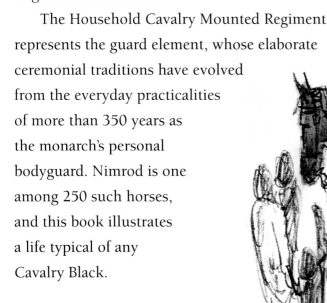

For the first few years of his life, the nameless foal who would become Nimrod, lived a carefree existence in Ireland, with a group of similar foals of the same age, his foal-mates.

Nimrod and his foal-mates were bred to become Cavalry Blacks, from parents chosen to produce horses likely to be big, strong, calm and black. Nimrod's sire (father) was a Thoroughbred and his dam (mother) was an Irish Draught – an ideal start. ᜪ

A ceremonial horse has to carry about 4 stone (25kg) in dead weight of kit, plus a man, amid excitable crowds in the noise and hustle of London, so a Cavalry Black is selected for strength as well as temperament.

Correct conformation (shape) is a great help to any horse. A Cavalry Black will usually be a gelding (no stallions), short-backed (to help carry the weight), at least 16 hands★ high at the withers (i.e. a minimum of about 5ft 4in, or 162cm, to the top of the spinal prominence in front of the saddle), but often bigger, up to about 17.2hh, and predominantly black. Ideally, he will also have a certain attitude of pride.

Nimrod himself was a perfectly true black, with no white markings on him at all. While his young friends fooled about in the field around him, Nimrod liked standing still and listening to the birds, thinking his own thoughts, enjoying the sun on his back. Some Cavalry Blacks seem naturally suited to life as a parade horse – born to it, in fact. ∽

★ A hand is a measurement by which the height of a horse is reckoned; each hand is 4in/10.6cm.

One day, when Nimrod and his friends were about four years old,
they had a rude awakening. The Riding Master of the Household Cavalry
arrived at the gate of their field. The Riding Master was accompanied by
some vets from the Royal Army Veterinary Corps, on their annual horse-
buying mission to Ireland.

They were looking for smart black horses who conformed to type
and were sound in wind and limb. Nimrod and his former foal-mates were
deemed good sorts. A large horsebox awaited. The moment had come
to leave the familiar quiet hills and head for a new life of clamour and
glamour. It was time for Nimrod to join the Army.

Once they had been examined by the vets and passed sound, the young horses were taken to Windsor, to acclimatise and begin their training.

The new horses were given official Household Cavalry names. Cavalry Blacks tend to be named after battles, places or something appropriately worthy, and each year, the new horses' names begin with a particular letter in sequence, in this case 'N'. The four new recruits were called Newburgh, Normandy, Neptune and NIMROD. Nimrod, as in Elgar's lament, played at the Cenotaph on Remembrance Day. Nimrod, as in 'Nimrod, the mighty hunter', in the Bible. 'N' for noble.

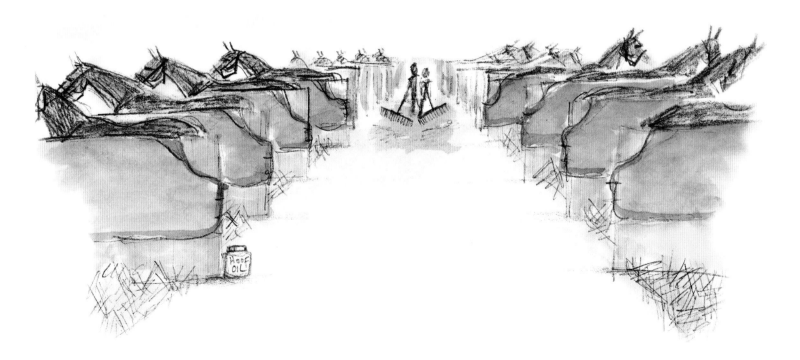

When a horse joins the Household Cavalry, he becomes a proper member of the regiment. He is given a regimental number, which is stamped on his hooves by a farrier. Nimrod's feet were stamped with his number and LG, for Life Guards.

An Army farrier always takes part in large parades and is identifiable by his axe (shown above left). Historically, the spike was to put a horse out of his misery if injured on the battlefield, and the axe was to cut off a dead horse's hoof as proof that he had actually died in battle, and had not been sold by an enterprising soldier. Several farriers are always on duty with the horses in Windsor and London, trained as farriers by the Army and fully qualified for this work in civilian life.

Nimrod was now all ready to start his education. At first, like any spirited young horse, Nimrod was easily spooked, but he soon became accustomed to the odd feeling of a bridle, a saddle, being lunged (going round in a circle on a long line) at different gaits and eventually being backed (having a rider on his back for the first time). Schooling, tack and 'horse furniture' (ceremonial kit) was gradually increased, until Nimrod could happily trot about in full ceremonial tack without any fear or fuss. ⌒♭

Meanwhile, on older and more experienced horses, new soldiers were learning to ride ...

Newly-recruited soldiers of the Household Cavalry Mounted Regiment – troopers – have riding lessons which typically start with having to vault onto their horses ('quickest and best' method to get on board). Troopers are of a minimum age of 17 and most have never ridden before at all. After 12 weeks of 'khaki ride', with many hours of trotting in circles with no stirrups, the soldiers progress to 4 weeks of 'kit ride', learning to ride effectively while wearing the full state kit of the Household Cavalry. After successfully completing a passing-out riding test, troopers are considered ready for ceremonial duties in London.

The Riding Master is an officer who began his career as a trooper and has been promoted 'up through the ranks' due to good riding and a natural affinity with horses. The Riding Master is responsible for the training of horses and riders, and thus for their performance on parade. This system is unique to the Household Cavalry, and it ensures that the Riding Master will always have had first-hand experience of all the complexities of kit preparation, tack cleaning, horse turnout and riding for several hours on a large parade.

After about 8 months of schooling by the Riding Master and his staff, Nimrod and his former foal-mates could be ridden calmly and had become recognisable as Household Cavalry horses, albeit still with the exuberance of youth, and with the inherent skittishness of being a horse. At this stage in his life, Nimrod was moved to London, ready to face the world.

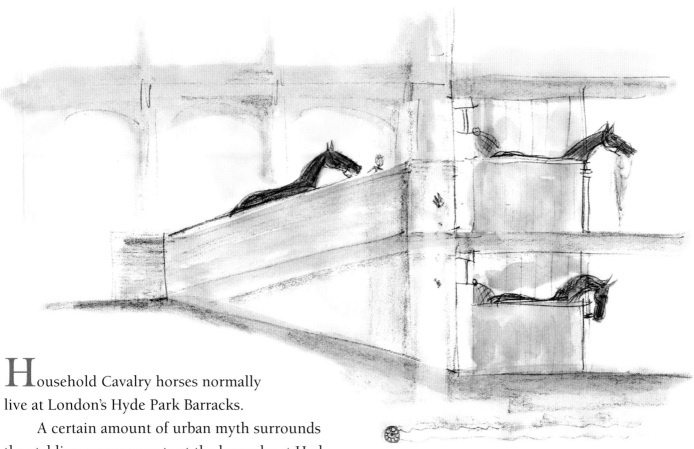

Household Cavalry horses normally
live at London's Hyde Park Barracks.

A certain amount of urban myth surrounds
the stabling arrangements at the barracks at Hyde
Park (more usually referred to as Knightsbridge Barracks).
There are rumours that the horses live in multi-storey stables, that mucking out is done
automatically, and that a secret conveyor belt takes the muck straight to the rose garden at
Buckingham Palace . . .

Some of these myths are actually true. ✍

The Household Cavalry takes pride in immaculate turnout. Every morning, before the daily guard change, an officer takes half an hour to inspect the troop – horse, man and kit. The officer will notice such details as:

- **on the horse** – coat, hooves picked out and oiled, tidy mane and tail, sponged nose and eyes;
- **on the rider** – the plume, helmet, boots and cuirass (breastplate);
- **on the kit** – the noseband, browband and brasses.

Many hours are spent cleaning kit. Boots gleam with layers of polish. White markings on horses are whitened with chalk. Brass details are cleaned with a toothpick. Learning to pay attention to detail in this way could later become a life-saving attribute when these same soldiers are on the battlefield.

Whenever the Household Cavalry rides from Knightsbridge Barracks to Horse Guards, to change the guard on duty, each man salutes the permanent memorial to the Hyde Park bombing, which killed four men and seven horses of the Household Cavalry in 1982. The memorial is sited in London's Hyde Park at the place where it happened. ✍

At eleven o'clock every morning, the changing of the guard takes place on Horse Guards Parade, alternating between The Life Guards and The Blues and Royals, and altering in numbers (long or short guard) according to whether or not the monarch is in London.

Historically, Horse Guards is the ceremonial entrance to the monarch's London home, and although that function is now more symbolic than actual, there are still some arcane rules restricting who may drive through the Horse Guards arch in a 'wheeled vehicle'. ∽

Each guard serves for 24 hours at a time, and is visibly on parade from 10am to 4pm, with each horse on duty for an hour at a time. The working stables in Horse Guards are viewable to the public from the Household Cavalry Museum, so men and horses must at all times conduct and deport themselves in a manner fitting for a member of The Queen's Life Guard, even when they are not actually on guard duty. ❧

Sometimes Nimrod's routine would be interrupted by a rude awakening at what seemed to be the middle of the night. Not being a morning person, Nimrod could be bit grumpy about being tacked up for a dress rehearsal at the crack of dawn. Yet these early-morning rehearsals heralded the great ceremonial occasions, when Nimrod would have to be on his best behaviour, events that would be his finest moments: the State Opening of Parliament, Trooping the Colour, a grand State Visit … in fact, the making of him. ᴗᴥᴑ

Just as Nimrod felt a bit weary with all his good behaviour, and just as London became full of heat and tourists, a convoy of Army horseboxes turned up and took all the horses on a holiday. It was time for the summer training camp in Norfolk. A month in the country and bareback galloping on the beach! The young horses were astounded. The older horses were rejuvenated. Everyone went for a swim in the sea.

Nimrod was a bold horse, so he swam quite far out to sea. The Norfolk beach-people watched in wonder, and Nimrod later appeared on the local news. The next day, Nimrod's picture was on the front page of several national newspapers, the photos aptly but incorrectly captioned as Neptune. The horse in the picture had an all-black head with no star, and could therefore not possibly be his old foal-mate Neptune.

Nimrod had taken to the daily routine of the Household Cavalry as naturally as a Hyde Park duck might take to the water in the Serpentine. It was as if it was all in his blood. Which, in fact, it was. While on his holidays, Nimrod practised the musical ride, a public show by the Household Cavalry, which is condensed enough to perform on show grounds. Nimrod enjoyed playing at being in the horse equivalent of the Red Arrows. It was fun. ∽

While Nimrod happily cantered this way and that, criss-crossing with his stable chums and their cohorts, the Monkey Men* performed their crowd-pleasing tricks – jumping through crossed lances, lying down with their horses, and casually standing up on their saddles. ∽

* Historically, the Monkey Men were the most expert horsemen, and demonstrated difficult skills to other troopers. Teaching their horses to lie down could provide cover for soldiers to hide behind on the battlefield.

As the holiday came to its end, the public visited for an open day. Nimrod and his stable mates had the seaweed brushed out of their tails. Buckets and spades were tidied up outside the tent-stables. Side shows and flags and people appeared. The horses and riders showed off their tent-pegging skills (a peculiar throwback from history) and did a bit of jumping. The grand finale was the musical ride, starring, among others, Nimrod. Ice-creams all round. It was a triumph.

Eventually, it was time to return to London. The horses of the King's Troop Royal Horse Artillery, who had been standing in for the Household Cavalry on guard duty, went home. Everything was back to normal. But the sea remained with Nimrod. He remembered the first waves of the morning, the feel of his body as he entered the cold water, and the freedom he found there – and the memory made him cheerful. The traffic noise in Hyde Park reminded him of the sea, and from then on Nimrod carried within him a Zen-like calm. ∽

BEWARE
HORSES MAY
KICK OR BITE
THANK YOU

The very first time Nimrod had stood all by himself for an hour on sentry duty as a 'boxman', he had felt lonely and instinctively nervous, as if separated from the herd in the wild, even though his foal-mate Neptune was nearby in the opposite box. But now, he enjoyed being photographed and admired and petted by tourists. He felt completely at home on Whitehall. It was on one such day that 'The Photograph' was taken, an image of a gleaming Nimrod in his prime, which would be reproduced for decades to come.

The routine of turnout inspections, guard changes, exercises, 'feed-aways', mucking-out, and so on, continued like clockwork. Nimrod jingled and jangled and clip-clopped along, as he trotted in line beside his old foal-mates, Newburgh, Normandy and Neptune. Older horses led the way at grand ceremonial occasions: the State Opening of Parliament; Trooping the Colour; the State Visit of the King of Somewhere. But the Riding Master had noticed Nimrod's constantly pricked ears, and the way that he always stood four-square and stock-still wherever he was placed on the parade ground. Good boy.

Nimrod had returned from his seaside holiday as a fully-mature parade horse. After that first season finding his feet in London, Nimrod was trusted with ever more public roles.

In any cavalcade of Household Cavalry troopers, it is easy to spot which are Life Guards and which are Blues and Royals. The most obvious way to recognise them is by the plumes: Life Guards, white; Blues and Royals, red. Also, the Life Guards' white plumes are topped with neat 'onions', and they wear red tunics, with smooth white sheepskins on their saddles. The Blues and Royals' red plumes have no 'onions', and they wear dark blue tunics, with shaggy black sheepskins on their saddles. The plumes are made of horse hair.

Over the next few years, Nimrod became the living embodiment of the classic image of a Household Cavalry horse, performing his daily duties at Horse Guards, and flying the flag for 'brand Great Britain' on parade and at grand state occasions. Nimrod could never have known or cared that he had appeared on telly and in newspapers all over the world. As a Cavalry Black, but never as an individual, Nimrod was a celebrity horse. ༄

'The Photograph' of Nimrod was reproduced in many guises and sizes – on postcards, books and biscuit tins; on mouse-mats, mugs and matchboxes; on key rings and phone covers. Nimrod even starred in a shoe-polish advertisement, featuring shiny black boots on a shiny black horse, as the shiniest shiny thing anyone could associate with black shoe polish.

As he approached 15, thoughts turned to Nimrod's retirement. After more than a decade of disciplined work as a public spectacle, with many turns at Trooping the Colour and the State Opening of Parliament, countless hours on guard duty, and a few unusual royal events, it was time to take life a bit more easily and be an ordinary horse again.

In retirement, some Cavalry Blacks just relax in a field with other horses at a retirement home. Nimrod was still fit and interested in life, so was more suited to an active country home where he might try a little 'winter training' and go out jumping big hedges. ∽

Horses generally enjoy having company and something
to do, so Nimrod enjoyed an active and sociable retirement
until he was about 25 years old. ❧

As he aged, Nimrod became less active, until eventually he was not ridden at all.

Keep an eye out for Nimrod on all those
postcards and royal wedding biscuit tins.
He'll be the black one.